MOBY DICK

Herman Melville

CAMPFIRE™

KALYANI NAVYUG MEDIA PVT LTD
New Delhi

Sitting around the Campfire, telling the story, were:

Wordsmith	:	Lance Stahlberg
Illustrator	:	Lalit Kumar Singh
Illustrations Editor	:	Jayshree Das
Colorist	:	Ajo Kurian
Letterer	:	Bhavnath Chaudhary
Editors	:	Eman Chowdhary
		Mark Jones
Research Editor	:	Pushpanjali Borooah
Production Controller	:	Vishal Sharma

Cover Artists:

Illustrator	:	Lalit Kumar Singh
Colorist	:	Ajo Kurian
Designer	:	Pushpa Verma

Published by Kalyani Navyug Media Pvt. Ltd.
101 C, Shiv House, Hari Nagar Ashram
New Delhi 110014
India
www.campfire.co.in

ISBN: 978-81-907515-0-6

Printed in India at Rave India

About the Author

Born on August 1, 1819 in New York City, USA, Herman Melville was a novelist, poet and short story writer.

From an early age, Melville was fascinated with words and stories. Even though a bout of scarlet fever left him with impaired eyesight, he continued to be a voracious reader and writer throughout his life.

Early in his working life he trained to be a surveyor and considered undertaking that profession as a career. However, the canal project he had been hoping to work on never transpired. Although, at the time, this appeared to be a setback for Melville, it was quite probably a blessing in disguise. Instead of working on a canal, he ended up as a cabin boy on board a merchant ship. This eventually led to him taking a job on a whaling vessel which traveled to the south seas.

As his sailing career continued, Melville wrote his first novel, *Typee*, in 1856. It was inspired by his life on the seas and contains many scenes plucked from his own experiences.

Melville's life was certainly just as full of drama and excitement as his novels. In 1847, he joined a mutiny on a ship where the crew were arguing with the owners over their share of the profits. For this, Melville was thrown into a jail in Tahiti. He escaped from the prison without too much difficulty and was later able to use the experience to write the novel entitled *Omoo*.

By this point in his literary career, Melville had enjoyed moderate praise for the novels he had authored. Then, in 1850, he published *Moby Dick*, which was sadly met with little enthusiasm at first. However, its popularity has increased greatly over time, particularly after his death, and is now regarded as one of the best-loved classics.

In his later years, Melville suffered due to ill health and the loss of two sons. As a consequence of these two hardships, he died in April 1891. His life had been a difficult one and his literary merits had reaped him little profit. Nowadays, however, he is widely considered to be one of the greatest American writers of all time.

QUEEQUEG

CAPTAIN AHAB

ISHMAEL

STARBUCK

STUBB

Call me Ishmael.

Some years ago—never mind how long exactly—having little or no money, I thought I would sail about a little and see the watery part of the world.

It is my way of driving off melancholy and participating in social life.

For whenever it is a damp, drizzly November in my soul, when it becomes difficult to stop myself lashing out at the world, then I know it's high time to get to sea as soon as I can.

But why did I want to go on a whaling voyage, after having been a merchant sailor for years? Only fate can answer that and no one else.

And, undoubtedly, going on a whaling voyage was only the beginning of the grand program that fate had planned for me.

But who am I to question fate...

...no matter where it leads me.

Spouter Inn

PETER COFFIN

Excuse me...
can I please meet
the landlord?

Hngh

I need
to meet the
landlord.

That'd be me.
My name is Peter
Coffin. If it's a room
you're looking for,
we're full.

No rooms
at all?

None.

But wait!

You've no objections
to sharing a harpooner's
blanket, have you? I suppose
you are going whale hunting,
so you'd better get used to
that sort of thing.

The next morning, I made my way downstairs.

Grub ho! Have some breakfast, Mr. Ishmael.

Good morning, Quee...

...queg.

Queequeg was looking at a book, but anyone could see that he didn't know how to read. I sat watching him with great interest.

Savage though he was, his appearance was by no means disagreeable. Through all his unearthly tattooings, I saw the traces of a simple, honest heart.

Would you like to know what the pages say?

You understand?

Yes. You want to understand?

Yes.

I soon engaged his interest, and from that we went on to chat about other things.

Queequeg told me of his home, Rokovoko, an island far away to the west and south. It is not shown on any maps.

True places never are.

Father... high chief, king. Uncle... high priest.

Many hunter, warrior deep in blood.

Queequeg had been a savage in his native land. Even then, a strong desire to see something more had lurked in his ambitious soul.

When a ship visited his father's bay and refused to take him on board, Queequeg made a vow.

Alone in his canoe, he paddled off to a distant strait, which he knew the ship would pass through.

As the ship was gliding by, he darted out like a flash, climbed up the chains, and threw himself upon the deck.

13

The captain threatened to throw him overboard, and slit his wrist with a cutlass, but Queequeg did not budge.

Struck by his courage, the captain relented. They put him down among the sailors and made a whaleman of him.

Before joining the ship, Queequeg had felt a profound desire to know more about civilized men, and behave like them.

But the practices of the whalers soon convinced him that even civilized men could be both miserable and wicked.

So, an old savage at heart, he lived among civilized men, wore their clothes, and tried to talk their gibberish. And that's the reason for his strange ways.

But you're the harpooner.

<Sigh>

Queequeg, you know how to kill a whale.

I don't. And I don't know what kind of ship to look for!

Just then, Queequeg noticed two people frowning at us and, before I could get up...

Boo!

Ahh!

Captain, captain, the devil's here.

What him say?

He thinks you will kill him.

Haha. Him small fish. Queequeg no kill so small fish; Queequeg kill big whale!

Just then, a strong wind began to pick up.

SNAP

And the prodigious strain on the main sail caused the rope to snap like a thin string.

For three minutes or more after he dived, Queequeg was seen swimming like a dog, throwing his long arms straight out before him, and revealing his brawny shoulders through the freezing water.

I watched the grand and glorious fellow, but could not see anyone to be saved.

Rising out of the water, Queequeg took a glance around him. He seemed to assess the situation and then he dived down...

...and disappeared!

Woohoo!! Hooray!!

A few minutes later, he rose again carrying a lifeless form.

Amazing.

The savage saved him!

From that hour, I clung to Queequeg like a barnacle.

Well done, Queequeg.

Queequeg did not seem to think he deserved a medal for what he had done. He only asked for water—fresh water—to wash the salt off.

Nothing more happened on that passage worthy of mention. So, after a fine run, we safely arrived in Nantucket.

Tell Yojo I understand. Me get good ship.

We then headed toward the *Try Pots Inn* which, according to Peter Coffin, was one of the best hotels in Nantucket.

Queequeg placed great confidence in the excellence of Yojo's judgement and forecast of things. And he cherished Yojo with considerable esteem.

But this plan of Queequeg's, or rather Yojo's, regarding the selection of our craft, was not to my liking at all.

I had relied greatly on Queequeg's expertise to describe the type of whaler best suited to carry us and our fortunes. With this knowledge, I began an energetic and determined search.

And then I found her.

One look and I knew this was the very ship for us.

Is this the captain of the *Pequod*?

Supposing it is the captain of the *Pequod*, what do you want from him?

I can, sir, if I must. But only if it's absolutely necessary to do so.

Why do you want to go? To see the world?

Yes, sir.

Well, there it is. Can't you see the world from where you stand?

Sir, I will go whaling. I must.

Though I'd rather it be on as fine a ship as the *Pequod*.

Then you may as well sign the papers right now! Come along.

On saying this, he led the way below deck into the cabin.

He says he's our man, Bildad. He wants to ship.

He does, does he?

I do!

He'll do, Peleg.

I have a friend who wants to ship, too. Shall I bring him tomorrow?

Well, bring him along. But I'm not your captain for this voyage.

My apologies. Then **you** must be cap--

No, son. I'm long retired.

It's up to me and Captain Peleg to ensure the *Pequod* is fitted out for the voyage. We are part owners and agents.

Fetch him along, and we will have a look at him. But has he whaled before?

Killed more whales than I can count, Captain Peleg.

Then who--

You haven't met nor even seen Captain Ahab yet, have you?

No. Who is Captain Ahab?

25

Captain Ahab is the captain of the ship.

You'll meet him soon. If you want to know what whaling is, as you say you do, I can show you a way to find out before you commit yourself to it past backing out.

One look at Captain Ahab, young man, and you will find that he has only one leg.

What do you mean, sir? Was the other one lost to a whale?

Lost to a whale! Young man, it was devoured, chewed up and crunched by the biggest monster that ever chipped a boat!

He doesn't speak much. But when he does, you best listen well.

Trust me.

Queequeg! You were right!

Woohoo!

I found it! I found our ship.

We set sail within the...

...week.

I had forgotten it was Queequeg's day of prayer. It seemed that it was some sort of Lent or Ramadan, or day of fasting.

Queequeg continued praying till the next morning.

Wake. Wake. Big day. We go.

Quick. Chop chop. Eat now, then go big ship.

So, after a hearty breakfast, we ran out to board the *Pequod*.

Stop! You, merchant sailor! No cannibals allowed on board the craft!

PEQUOD

What's this? No... no. He must show his papers.

He must show that he's converted.

What do you mean by that?

Is he in communion with a church?

My friend Queequeg is a member of the First Congregational Church.

How long has he been a member? Not very long I gue--

Saints above!

Suddenly, Queequeg jumped off the plank and onto the deck.

Captain, you see him small drop tar on water? You see him? Well, think him one whale eye, well, then!

If he whale then he dead whale now.

Shipmates, have you shipped in that ship yet?

You mean on the *Pequod*?

Yes. Have you?

We have recently signed the papers.

Papers, eh? Anything in them about your souls?

About what?

Oh, perhaps you haven't got any. It doesn't matter. I know many chaps that haven't got any, and they are all the better for it.

What are you jabbering about?

He's got enough to make up for all deficiencies of that sort in other chaps, though.

All about it, eh?

Sure you do? All?

Pretty sure.

And about them?

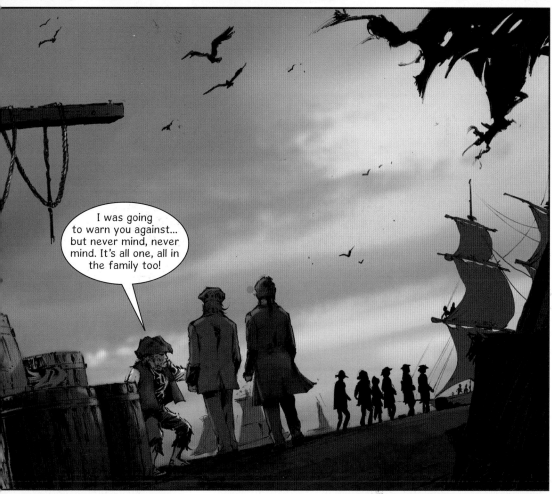

I was going to warn you against... but never mind, never mind. It's all one, all in the family too!

Morning to you, shipmates!

33

The next morning, we boarded the *Pequod*.

About time, mates. We hoist sails today.

You're the second mate, right?

We haven't formally met. I'm--

I know who you are.

There's nothing formal about the *Pequod*. Just listen up and do as you're told.

My name's Stubb, second mate. Your first mate over there is Starbuck.

I heard the captain came aboard last night. Is he feeling well?

Now there's an interesting question.

He's aboard. But don't disturb him if you value your life.

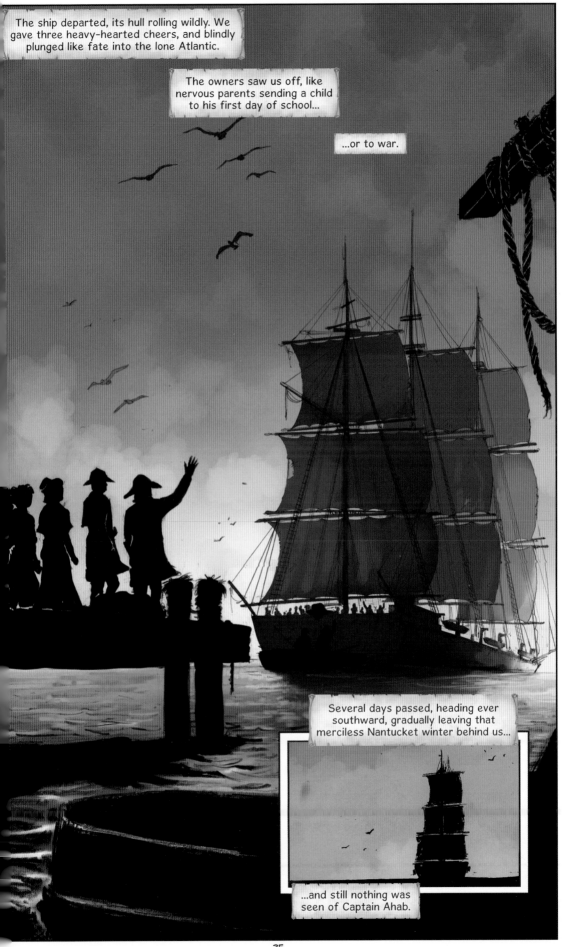

The ship departed, its hull rolling wildly. We gave three heavy-hearted cheers, and blindly plunged like fate into the lone Atlantic.

The owners saw us off, like nervous parents sending a child to his first day of school...

...or to war.

Several days passed, heading ever southward, gradually leaving that merciless Nantucket winter behind us...

...and still nothing was seen of Captain Ahab.

The mates took turns to keep watch, and seemed to be the only commanders of the ship. But sometimes they came from the cabin with orders so sudden and decisive that it was clear they commanded vicariously.

Their supreme lord and dictator was there, though unseen by any eyes not permitted to penetrate into the sacred retreat of the cabin.

Many said Captain Ahab was a myth made up by the mates to keep us in line.

Until...

THUNK

THUNK

THUNK

THUNK

...reality outran apprehension.

40

But all of the legends paled in comparison to the story of the first meeting of the leviathan of the deep and Captain Ahab.

Ever since that almost fatal encounter, Ahab had cherished a wild vindictiveness against the whale.

'Yes! I lost this leg,' he'd said. 'And I now prophesy that I will dismember my dismemberer.'

Then, one day, in our third month at sea...

There she blows!

Where is he?

Who?

Moby Dick, of course!

It's not Moby Dick, sir. There's a whole school of them!

Permission to lower boats, Captain?

Lower away.

Such was the thunder of his voice that within seconds the men sprang over the rail, the boats were dropped into the sea and the sailors leaped into them.

Spread yourselves out and pull out to leeward.

Wa ka-la kooloo!!

Steady now...

Steady...

Pull, men! There, there she blows again!

That's the hump. Give it to him, Queequeg!

A short rushing sound leaped out of the boat—it was the darted iron of Queequeg.

Got him!

Wet the line! Wet the line!

As soon as we had secured the rope, harpooners from the other boats attacked the whale.

Stern all!

Haul us in, boys! Haul in!

You know, Queequeg, I always wondered why people hunted such a dangerous creature.

Recently, I came to know that the reason was ambergris. Ambergris—extracted from whale fat—is highly fragrant, and widely used in expensive perfumes, pastilles, precious candles and hair powders.

But then, what reward doesn't come with a price?

After the whale was chained to the side of the ship, a series of nets and platforms were suspended by ropes to haul the meat and blubber up.

47

As the expedition continued, I learned about something that whaling ships generally involve themselves in. Something called the gam.

Let's ask them, sir.

The gam is a social meeting between two or more whaling vessels at sea.

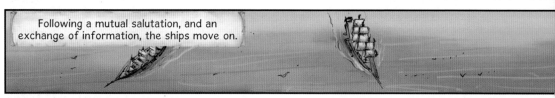

Have you seen the white whale?

And it is a thing so utterly unknown to all other ships that they've never even heard the name.

Following a mutual salutation, and an exchange of information, the ships move on.

Stay course.

Still no sign of Moby Dick, sir.

We'll find him, Starbuck, don't you worry.

Then, one day, after turning north beyond Cape Horn...

There... there again! There she breaches!

It's him! A great white hump ahead to starboard!

Moby Dick. I knew we'd find you.

Lower the boats!

I have you now, Moby Dick!

Face me, Moby Dick!

And then...

Later that week, we learned that the ship's passage through the icy Antarctic had proven more costly than we knew.

Who's there? Be gone.

Captain Ahab; it is I, Starbuck.

The oil in the hold is leaking, sir. We must break out.

Break out? After having come so far, break out?

No. Let it leak.

Then we will waste more oil in a day than we may make good in a year.

What we came twenty thousand miles to get is worth saving, sir.

So it is...

...if we get it.

I was speaking of the oil in the hold, sir.

Yes. I suppose you would be. Begone. Let it leak!

What will the owners say, sir?

Let the owners stand on Nantucket beach and outyell the typhoons. I don't care!

Owners, owners? You are always babbling to me, Starbuck, about those miserly owners, as if the owners were my conscience. But, remember, the only real owner of anything is its commander...

...and listen, your commander's conscience is in this ship's keel.

On deck. Now!

I do not question your conscience, sir. I only--

There is one God that is Lord over the Earth, and one Captain that is Lord over the *Pequod*. On deck.

You have outraged, but not insulted me, sir. I ask you not to beware of Starbuck...

...but let Ahab beware of Ahab. Beware of yourself, old man.

He talks bravely, but nevertheless obeys.

Most careful bravery that.

He said Ahab beware of Ahab. He's got something there.

You are too good a fellow, Starbuck.

Tell the crew to break out in the main hold.

Yes, sir.

It is hard to say exactly why Ahab had a change of heart. Nevertheless, his command was carried out.

We were ordered to break the casks out from the hold and check which were leaking.

How are they looking, Perth?

These are all in good condition, sir.

We need to find that leak. Keep looking.

Upon searching, it was found that the first casks were perfectly sound and the leak must be further off. So, we started to check the casks deeper in the hold.

Step lively, boys!

Queequeg, who was already seized with fever, could not take the strain and...

Queequeg? You don't look well.

Queequeg!!

Let's get him to a hammock.

He must not have coped with the Antarctic air as well as he let on. It seems the chill had sapped his strength.

You're going to be okay.

Suddenly, Ahab turned to Perth and the carpenter.

Perth! Fashion me a harpoon, my friend.

Make it twelve rods strong.

Forge the rods together for its shank.

Perth, what about--

Don't ask questions. Just fetch me the rods.

Below deck, Queequeg was not faring too well.

He's delirious.

Ishmael, please...

Ishmael, make me a--

No, my friend. Don't ask me to do that.

Back on the deck...

Here. I will neither shave nor eat until the white whale is dead.

I want that harpoon. And I want Moby Dick dead!

Queequeg wants a coffin. While in Nantucket, he saw some small canoes made of dark wood. He came to know that all whalemen who died in Nantucket were laid in those canoes. The idea really pleased him.

He hates the thought of being buried in his hammock, to be food for the sharks, according to the usual sea custom.

Once the harpoon, which had been forged to kill Moby Dick, was complete, Ahab baptized it.

Ego non baptizo te in nomine patris...

...sed in nomine diaboli!*

HHIISSS

*In English: I baptize you, not in the name of the Father, but in the name of the devil.

And when the coffin was made, Queequeg leaned over in his hammock, and regarded it with an attentive eye.

But I forbade him from using it.

Later, there was a gam with a British ship.

Of course, I knew there could only be one reason why we stopped for it.

Yes, I saw his wake again. Twice.

But you could not fasten, Boomer?

58

'Sunward', he had ordered.

Was it another sign, then, that the sun disappeared within the hour?

I wonder how many we needed.

Listen! The white flame of heaven leads us to the white whale! I hear you, my sire!

Leap! Leap up and lick the sky! I leap with you! I burn with you! My fate is welded with you! Defiantly, I worship you!

And like a true child of fire, I breathe it back to you!

God is against you, old man! Give in. This is an ill voyage! Ill begun, ill continued!

Let me turn us around while we still can, and make haste to a better voyage than this!

No, Starbuck!

In a fit of anger, Ahab grabbed the harpoon, swinging it toward Starbuck.

KRA-THOOM

But before the harpoon could reach Starbuck, lightning struck the metal.

I own you speechless, placeless power. Did I not say so?

Ahab continued to wave the harpoon like a torch.

Look, my dear friends!

All your oaths to hunt the white whale are as binding as mine...

...by heart, soul, lungs and life, old Ahab is bound! And so you may know to what tune this heart beats...

...look here as this fear is extinguished.

At this, many of the men ran away from Ahab in the terror of dismay.

It was through no small effort by the ship's mates that the *Pequod* survived that storm.

As for her captain...

...Starbuck reluctantly, gloomily and mechanically went below to apprise Captain Ahab of the situation.

Captain...

Strange! I have handled so many deadly lances, so why am I shaking now?

I have come to report a fair wind to him. But how fair? Fair for death and doom—that's fair for Moby Dick. A fair wind is only fair for that accursed whale!

The very gun he pointed at me—the very one. He would have killed me with it. And he would gladly kill all his crew.

Stern all... oh Moby Dick, I clutch your heart at last.

Is heaven a murderer when its lightning strikes a would-be murderer in his bed? And would I be a murderer if...

But Starbuck couldn't do it!

He's sound asleep, Mr. Stubb.

Give him another hour and then wake him. You know what to say. I must see to the deck here.

Queequeg!

See Yojo in dream. Him say not day to die.

What me miss?

So I spent the whole day telling him what had happened while he was unwell.

The next morning, Ahab made an appearance.

What is this?

I made up this thing here as a coffin for Queequeg, but now they've got me to turn it into a lifebuoy. Mr. Starbuck's orders.

Are you not also the leg maker? Did my stump come from your shop?

I believe it did. How is it, sir?

Just fine. You are a true artisan.

Thank you, sir.

Sailor... where are we heading?

Due east, Captain.

Liar!

East at this hour in the morning and the sun astern?

Every man was confused, as the phenomenon observed by Ahab had escaped everyone else's attention.

Fix this compass.

It is not uncommon for accidents like this to occur in violent storms. The magnetic energy in the mariner's needle can be spoiled by lightning.

Do you know which way the sun rises?

Uh... yes, sir.

Time and tide flow wide, sir. Moby Dick has the whole round watery world to swim in, as the small goldfish has its glassy globe.

I know his latitudes, Starbuck.

I know where he can go, every sea-shelled ground and volcano bay.

He has outrageous strength with inscrutable malice. That inscrutable thing is chiefly what I hate.

And I will wreak that hate upon him. Mark my words.

You speak of a dumb beast.

To be enraged with a dumb thing is blasphemy.

Don't speak to me of blasphemy. I'd strike the Sun if it insulted me.

What of your wife? By God, Captain, you must want to see your son again.

Mr. Starbuck, until this is done, my boy's face is to me as the palm of my hand...

...a lipless, unfeatured blank.

Ship ahoy!

It is Moby Dick. He is responsible for it.

He's not dead then? Not killed?

Ahab, listen to me!

I will not go till you say yes to me.

Do to me as you would have me do to you in a similar situation. For you too have a boy, Captain Ahab, nestling safely at home.

You relent, Ahab. I see it.

Hurry men! Run now and--

Stop!

RACH

Turning hurriedly, Ahab descended into his cabin to avoid any further confrontation with Gardiner.

When three or four days had passed by, and no spout had yet been seen, Ahab became distrustful of his crew's fidelity.

He seemed to think his men might willingly overlook the sight he sought.

I'll have the first sight of the whale myself.

Captain?

Stand aside, matey.

Your hat, your hat, sir!

But, no matter what he thought, he cleverly refrained from saying it, even though his actions seemed to hint it.

The first time Ahab was perched aloft, a savage sea hawk came wheeling and screaming around his head in a maze of swift circling.

It darted a thousand feet straight up into the air, then spiraled downward...

...and fled with its prize.

Mr. Starbuck, remember, stay on board and keep the ship.

Yes, sir.

Move! Move!

He's heading straight to leeward, sir. Right away from us!

He can't have seen the ship yet.

Come on, men. Waste no time. Hard after him.

Soon all the boats were dropped, and with rippling swiftness the men set out to hunt Moby Dick.

He lay a little distance away, vertically thrusting his oblong head up and down in the billows, and slowly revolving his body.

Men, steady. Silent but swift, before he turns flukes.

Moby Dick soon resumed his horizontal position, and swam swiftly around and around the crew, churning the water sideways in his vengeful wake. It was as if he was building himself up to a deadly assault.

Drive him off!

Sail on the whale!

77

Forehead to forehead I meet you again, Moby Dick! There is nowhere left to run!

Before Ahab could throw the harpoon...

...Moby Dick's movements overturned Stubb's boat.

But the men did not retreat.

Got him!

Tashtego has him!

Moby Dick suddenly rolled his body against the boat and, without damaging it, turned it over. Had it not been for the gunwale to which Ahab then clung, he would have been tossed into the sea.

Heaven help us all.

Retribution, swift vengeance, eternal malice were his whole being. In spite of all that mortal man could do, his solid white forehead struck the ship's starboard bow, and men and timbers reeled.

Through dim, bewildering vision, Ahab saw the sidelong fading phantom. The ship's crew and everything else rolled around and around in a whirlpool till the smallest chip of the *Pequod* was out of sight.

I am coming for you, Moby Dick! I will wrestle with you till I have killed you!

For hate's sake, I spit my last breath at you.

The harpoon was darted and the whale flew forward. The line ran with such velocity. Ahab stooped to clear it...

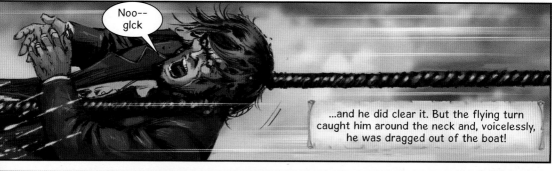

Noo-- glck

...and he did clear it. But the flying turn caught him around the neck and, voicelessly, he was dragged out of the boat!

When I saw Ahab pulled under the water by that monster, I knew he was gone for good.

It so happened that, after the captain's disappearance, the tide brought me to the surface.

The coffin lifebuoy shot lengthwise from the sea and floated by my side.

Buoyed up by that coffin for almost one whole day and night, I floated on.

On the second day, a sail drew near, and picked me up at last. It was the *Rachel*, Captain Gardiner's ship.

In her search for her missing children, she had only found another orphan.

CONQUERING EVEREST

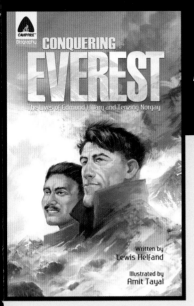

A graphic biography of Edmund Hillary and Tenzing Norgay

Written by Lewis Helfand
Illustrated by Amit Tayal

Tenzing Norgay was the son of poor Tibetan immigrants living in Nepal. He wished to see the world, but was told he could aspire to be little more than a servant.

Edmund Hillary was a humble beekeeper from New Zealand, who spent his youth dreaming of adventures he could never hope to experience.

And Everest was the ultimate adventure. The mountain's peak was the highest point on Earth, stretching beyond the clouds. Dangerous and challenging, Everest had never been successfully climbed, and many had died trying. In 1953, Tenzing Norgay and Edmund Hillary joined a team of explorers determined to reach its top.

Alone at the top of the world, with their oxygen running low, they encountered brutal elements and new dangers at every turn. And they were armed with little more than their courage, determination, and belief in each other. But would that be enough to achieve the impossible—what no man had ever done before?

It is not the mountain we conquer but ourselves.
Edmund Hillary

Dreams are illustrations... from the book your soul is writing about you.
Tenzing Norgay

WHALE HO!

SPERM WHALE

The sperm whale is the largest of all toothed whales. Usually gray or brown in color, it has a huge head which accounts for one-third of its body, and which contains more than a thousand liters of oily fluid called spermaceti. Weighing about nine kilograms, the sperm whale's brain is the largest of any living creature. It's even bigger than the brain of the giant blue whale! Interestingly, the sperm whale is also the marine mammal which can dive the deepest, and is known to plunge to depths of up to 4,000 feet in search of its favorite food—the giant squid. During these dives, it often holds its breath for more than an hour! The sperm whale travels in groups called pods and the members of a pod communicate with each other by making loud clicking sounds.

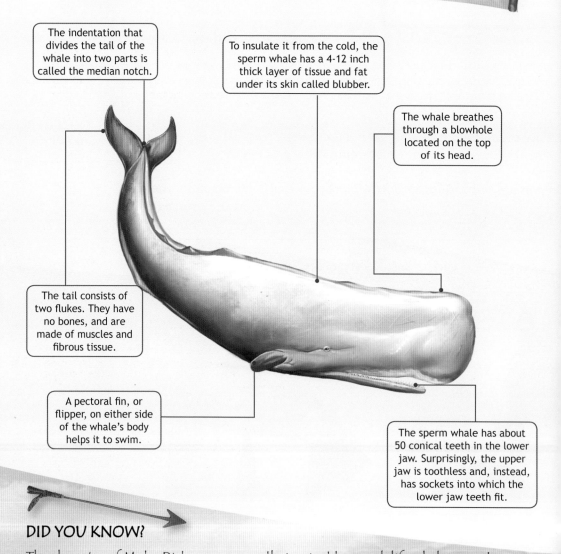

The indentation that divides the tail of the whale into two parts is called the median notch.

To insulate it from the cold, the sperm whale has a 4-12 inch thick layer of tissue and fat under its skin called blubber.

The whale breathes through a blowhole located on the top of its head.

The tail consists of two flukes. They have no bones, and are made of muscles and fibrous tissue.

A pectoral fin, or flipper, on either side of the whale's body helps it to swim.

The sperm whale has about 50 conical teeth in the lower jaw. Surprisingly, the upper jaw is toothless and, instead, has sockets into which the lower jaw teeth fit.

DID YOU KNOW?

The character of Moby Dick was supposedly inspired by a real-life whale named Mocha Dick. Mocha Dick was a huge white sperm whale that lived in the Pacific Ocean in the 19th century. Named after the island of Mocha near Chile, many accounts say that it killed more than 30 men and destroyed several ships! Like Moby Dick, it escaped countless attacks from whalers, and survived dozens of harpoons being thrown into its back. Mocha Dick was eventually killed in the 1830s.

THE 19th CENTURY WHALER

Whaling, or the hunting of whales, flourished in Britain and America during the 19th century. Oil, bones, and meat were all valuable commodities that were acquired by capturing whales. Sperm whales, in particular, were hunted for spermaceti, which was used in many things like lamp fuel, perfumes, and candles. The 19th-century whaler was a ship, especially designed for whaling. Not only did it carry the equipment for hunting and killing its prey, but also the facilities for processing, storing, and preserving it until its return to port. It was a large ship and was spacious enough to store provisions for long voyages as well as the yield from a hunt.

The captain's cabin was located at the rear of the ship.

Whaleboats were small boats, used by the sailors to get as close as possible to the whale in order to throw their harpoons.

The steerage was located above the cargo hold. It was a dark and cramped living area used by ordinary sailors.

Try pots were large iron pots in which blubber was melted into oil.

The blubber room was a dark room where the whale's blubber was cut into pieces and prepared for boiling.

The storage space of the whaler was called the hold and was located in the lower part of the interior of the ship's hull. Provisions, spare sails and ropes were stored there.

The whale oil, as well as fresh water, was stored in barrels.

DID YOU KNOW?

In their spare time, the crew of whalers carved beautiful designs on the teeth of sperm whales. This art was called scrimshaw. Figures were carved on the surface of a whale's tooth with a knife or needle, and then filled in with ink. Most sailors carved whaling scenes and their loved ones.